HARMONY IS FUN

BOOK 2

Maureen Cox

Kate Hewson

2-75.

First published 1999
by **Subject Publications**
Beech House
Broadstone
Dorset BH18 9NJ
Tel: +44 (0)1202 696907
Fax: +44 (0)1202 657743

ISBN 1 898771 14 6

Printed by Pardy & Son (Printers) Ltd.,
Parkside, Ringwood, Hampshire, BH24 3SF
Tel: +44 (0)1425 471433
Fax: +44 (0)1425 478923

Authors' note

This book is the second in a series of three books. In Book 1 you met the **root position** and **first inversion chords** of the **Inner Family - Mother, Father** and **Daughter -** and used them to harmonise melodies.

In this book you will meet **second inversion chords** and three more musical family members. We shall introduce you to **Cousin, Grandmother** and **Grandfather**.

The **C, F** and **G Major Families** are joined in this book by four more neighbours from the magic circle of keys. These are the families of **D Major, A Major, B♭ Major** and **E♭ Major**. You will also meet their **Minor Relatives**.

With our help you will learn to play a greater variety of melodies with richer sounding chords using a keyboard. Once again you will discover with this book that Harmony is Fun.

Acknowledgements

We are grateful to Subject Publications for inviting us to write this second book and thereby giving us the opportunity to continue the rewarding task of conveying to others the excitement and enjoyment of harmony.

We should particularly like to express our thanks to Brenda Harris for her enthusiastic support and to Alison Hounsome for her meticulous study of our manuscript and her most constructive comments.

Maureen Cox & Kate Hewson

CONTENTS

Well-known Families   6

More Next-door Neighbours   7

The Inner Family with New Keys   8

Key Signatures in the Bass Clef   11

Roman Numerals   14

Dominant 7th Chord   16

Root Position Chords   17

First Inversion Chords   18

Second Inversion Chords   19

Harmonising a Melody   25

Some Minor Relatives   28

The Supertonic   32

The Mediant   36

The Submediant   40

Resolving   46

Block Chords   48

Broken Chords and Pedalling   49

Three Tunes to Harmonise   52

Three Harmonisations to Play   55

Major & Harmonic Minor Scales   58

The Magic Circle of Keys   60

List of Terms   61

Well-known Families

In Book 1 you met three families.

This began the **Magic Circle of Keys**.

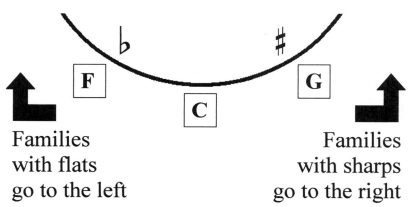

Families
with flats
go to the left

Families
with sharps
go to the right

In this book you will meet some
more neighbours so that you can
expand the magic circle of keys and
increase your harmonising abilities.

More Next-door Neighbours

 D Major Family has 2 sharps: F♯ & C♯

 A Major Family has 3 sharps: F♯, C♯ & G♯

 B♭ Major Family has 2 flats (B♭ & E♭)

 E♭ Major Family has 3 flats (B♭, E♭ & A♭)

The **Magic Circle of Keys** has grown.

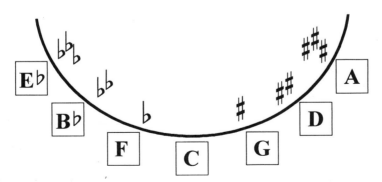

The Inner Family with New Keys

Here are the notes in the **D Major** Family with the Mother, Daughter and Father chords.

Use your right hand to play

Mother's chord   Daughter's chord

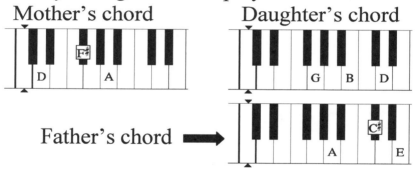

Father's chord ➡

Now repeat the exercise for the **E♭ Major** Family. Remember there are three flats.

Play each chord with your right hand and listen to their sounds.

Getting to Know the New Keys

Draw **with** key signatures:

Mother's chord in the
A Major Family ➔

Father's chord in the
← **E♭ Major** Family.

Daughter's chord in the
B♭ Major Family ➔

Father's chord in the
← **D Major** Family

Daughter's chord in the
E♭ Major Family ➔

Play each chord after you have drawn it.

Remember the Sharps and Flats

Draw **without** key signatures but put in any necessary sharps or flats:

Mother's Chord
[the Tonic]
in **D Major** ➔

Daughter's chord
[the Subdominant]
← in **E♭ Major**

Father's chord
[the Dominant]
in **A Major** ➔

Daughter's chord
[the Subdominant]
← in **B♭ Major**

Play each chord. Does it sound right? Check for those sharps and flats.

Key Signatures in the Bass Clef

It is important to be absolutely sure of your key signatures. That means knowing where to place sharps or flats in the **bass clef** as well as in the treble clef.

Write these key signatures in the **bass clef**:

D Major

B♭ Major

A Major

E♭ Major

Look at page 7 to check your answers.

Using Treble and Bass Clefs

Here are Mother, Daughter and Father chords in the **D Major** Family. Using both hands, play and listen to these chords.

Fill in the notes in the treble clef for the Mother, Daughter and Father chords in the **A Major** Family. Play and listen to these chords.

Here are the **root** notes for Mother, Daughter and Father chords in the **E♭ Major** Family. Add the notes in the treble clef. Play and listen to these chords.

Harmony with the Inner Family

Here is a tune for you to play and enjoy. It has the three chords of the **Inner family** of **D Major**. Remember to play the **sharps.**

Here is a similar tune in **E♭ Major**. Don't forget to play the **flats**.

Roman Numerals

So far we have been writing 1, 4 and 5 for Mother [Tonic], Daughter [Subdominant] and Father [Dominant] chords.

These numbers are more usually written as **Roman Numerals I, IV** and **V**. Let's get used to them now.

I  IV  V

Draw in the **Inner Family** chords for **E♭ Major**.

Now draw the **Inner Family** chords for **A Major**.

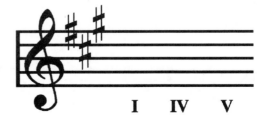

Harmonise these Melodies

Draw Mother, Daughter and Father chords for each of these melodies. First put the **root** note of each chord **in the bass** clef for your **left** hand. Play each piece with both hands, counting carefully. Listen to the melody and harmony.

A tune in **E♭ Major**

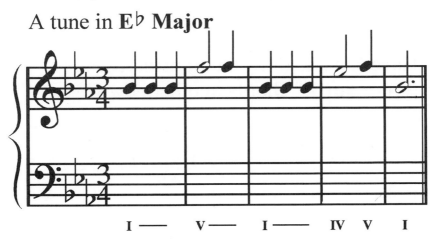

A tune in **A Major**

Father's Dominant 7th Chord

So far we have used the Inner Family chords without the **Dominant 7th** chord. Here are Father's two chords in **D Major**.

Have fun and draw the **dominant** and **dominant 7th** chords in other new keys:

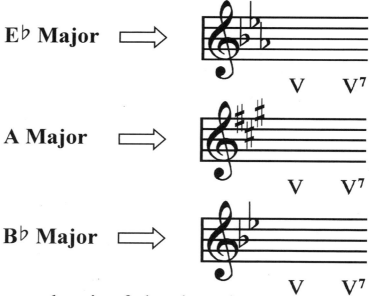

E♭ Major

A Major

B♭ Major

Play each pair of chords and listen to their different sounds.

Root Position

In Book 1 you learnt to draw **root position** chords in two different ways. Draw the **closed** and **open** chords for the **Inner Families** of **D Major** and **E♭ Major**. All the **roots** and two **tonic** chords have been drawn for you.

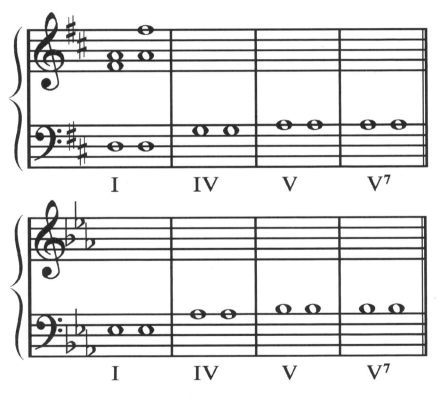

For the open V^7 chords, you may need to play two of the notes with your left hand.

First Inversion

You learnt in Book 1 that a **first inversion** chord has the **3rd at the bottom**.

Here is Mother chord in **A Major** in **root position** and in **first inversion**.

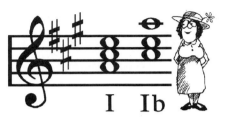

I   Ib

 b = 3rd at the bottom of the chord

Draw Daughter chord in **E♭ Major**

IV   IVb

in **root position** and in **first inversion**.

Now draw the **Dominant 7th** chord for

Father in **B♭ Major** in **root position** and in **first inversion**.

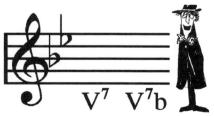

V^7 V^7b

Play each chord and listen to the sound.

Second Inversion

A **second inversion** has the **5ᵗʰ at the bottom** and a letter **c** with the chord number.

Here is Mother chord in **C Major** drawn in

root position [I]
first inversion [Ib]
second inversion [Ic]

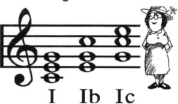

I Ib Ic

☀ **c = 5th at the bottom of the chord**

Play the following chords.

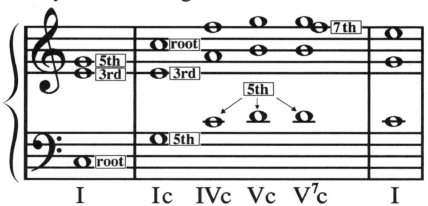

I   Ic   IVc Vc   V⁷c   I

☀ In any chord, the **order of notes above** the **bottom note** can often be changed.

A Quick Look Back

The D Family has ____ sharps. Its next-door-neighbour ___ Major has 3 ____.
The ___ Major Family has 2 flats. Its next-door neighbour ___ Major has ____ flats.
In every musical family _____ chord is the tonic with the Roman numeral I.
Daughter chord is the _____ with the Roman numeral ____. Father chord is the _____ with the Roman numeral ____ . Father chord can have an extra note, seven up from the root: his chord is then called the _____ 7th.

12

Fill in the gaps with help from the letters and words in the box.

| c | second | b | inversion | 3rd | /5 |

A first inversion chord has the ____ note of the chord at the bottom. A _____ inversion chord has the 5th at the bottom. First inversion chords have the letter ___ after the Roman numeral. Chords followed by the letter ___ are known as second _____ chords.

Take Care!

Sometimes, a chord within one family has the same notes as a chord within another.

Mother E♭ and **Daughter B♭** are *different* people.

Always look at the key signature to identify the family.

Root, 1st and 2nd Inversions

Here are the **B♭ Major** Family chords in **root position**, **first inversion** and **second inversion**. Notice that the **root**, **3rd** or **5th** is at the bottom of the chord. Play the chords.

Now draw the chords for the **Inner Family** of **E♭ Major**. Father's **dominant 7th** chord and the bottom notes, **root**, **3rd** or **5th**, have been drawn for you. Play all these chords.

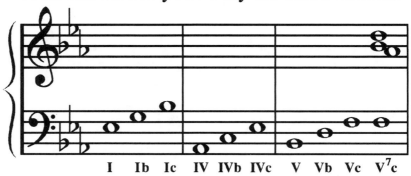

Practice Makes Perfect

Draw the chords for the **Inner Family** of **G Major** in **root position**, **first inversion** and **second inversion**. The bottom notes, **root**, **3rd** or **5th**, have been drawn for you.

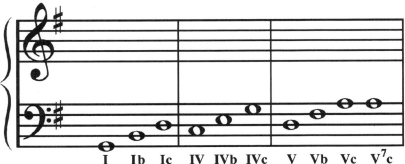

I   Ib   Ic   IV IVb IVc   V Vb Vc V^{7}c

Now draw the chords for the **Inner Family** of **A Major** and play them.

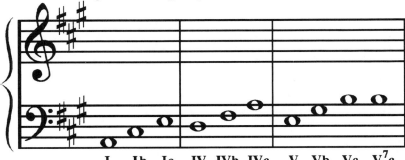

I   Ib   Ic   IV IVb IVc   V Vb Vc V^{7}c

Practise these chords in all keys. This will help you to move easily between musical families in the magic circle of keys.

Drawing Chords for Melodies

Here are melody notes from the **tonic**, **dominant**, **subdominant** and **dominant 7th** chords in four major keys. Draw in the missing notes, shared between the two hands, to complete the harmonies.

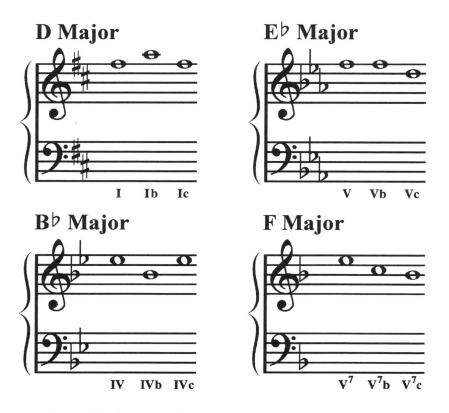

D Major

I   Ib   Ic

E♭ Major

V   Vb   Vc

B♭ Major

IV   IVb   IVc

F Major

V⁷   V⁷b   V⁷c

Play all the chords and listen to the sounds.

Harmonising a Melody

Here is a melody in the key of **E♭ Major**. Play the melody and listen to it.

Here is the same melody with harmony. Put the **missing chord names** in the six boxes.

I   IV ☐ Ib ☐☐ Ib ☐ IV ☐ Ic ☐ I

Check your answers.

6

ᴧ qI I ᴧ ᴧI ɔᴧ

Now play the harmonised melody and listen to the difference in the sound. Notice that we double some notes and we do not use the second inversion very often.

Over to You

Here are chords in the key of **B♭ Major**. Put their names in the ten empty boxes.

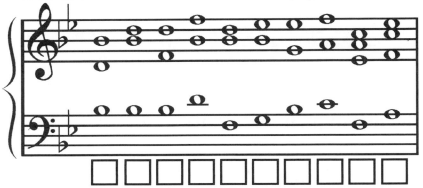

Use the chords to harmonise the melody below using minims and crotchets. The chord numbers are given to help you.

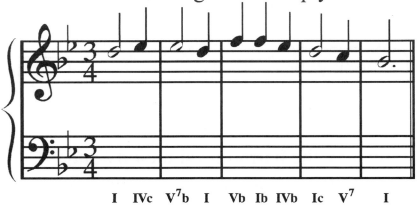

I   IVc   V⁷b   I   Vb   Ib   IVb   Ic   V⁷   I

Play your harmonised melody.

The Ultimate Test

Here are all the melody notes from the chords you have met so far in the **C Major** and **D Major** Families. Fill in the missing notes, shared between the two hands, to complete the harmonies. Play your chords.

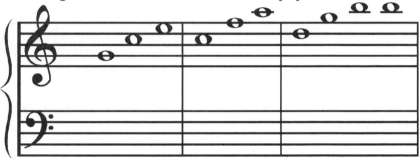

I   Ib   Ic   IV   IVb   IVc   V   Vb   Vc   V⁷c

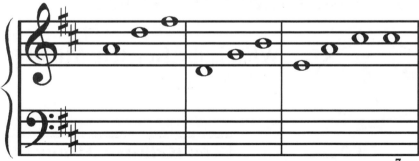

I   Ib   Ic   IV   IVb   IVc   V   Vb   Vc   V⁷c

Now that you can draw **root position**, **first inversion** and **second inversion** chords for familiar keys, you are ready to meet a new set of related families.

Meet Some Minor Relatives

Each **Major** Family is related
to a **Minor** Family.

For example, **C Major** and
A Minor are related. Count down
three semitones from **C**
on the keyboard and you reach **A**.

C Major and **A Minor** have
the same key signature -
no sharps or flats.

Discover More Relatives

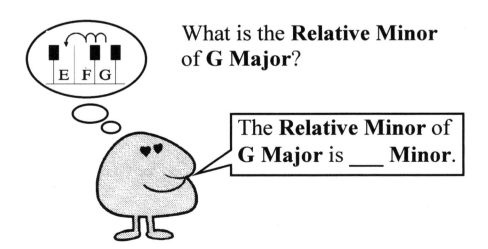

What is the **Relative Minor**
of **G Major**?

The **Relative Minor** of
G Major is ___ **Minor**.

 **D Major** is related to
B Minor

Count three semitones to find the missing relatives.

Fill in these key signatures in both clefs.

 B♭ Major is related to
____ Minor

 A Major is related to
____ Minor

 F Major is related to
____ Minor

 E♭ Major is related to
____ Minor

With the Minor Families, you have the key to unlock a whole new world of harmony.

Minor Differences

To understand the differences between
Major and **Minor** Families you have to
look at all their notes. Here is the scale of
C Major going up ↑ then down ↓.

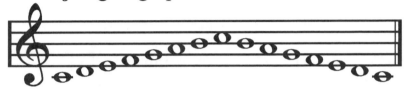

Here is the scale of **A Harmonic Minor**.
The **7**[th] note has been raised by one
semitone ascending ↑ and descending ↓.

Play the two scales and listen as you play.
Harmonies and tunes in a Minor key may
sound sadder than those in a Major key.

There are two forms of Minor scale. In this
book the **Harmonic Minor Scales** of all your
new Minor Families are on pages 58 and 59.
You will meet the **Melodic** form in Book 3.

Drawing Minor Family Chords

Can **you** draw the **root position** chords for the **Inner Family** of **D Minor**? Remember to raise the 7th note in minors: see ☺ below.

E Minor   **D Minor**

I   I

IV   IV

V ☺   V

V⁷ ☺   V⁷

A Visit from a Cousin

So far you have met the **Inner Family**.

Chord I	Tonic
Chord IV	Subdominant
Chord V	Dominant
Chord V⁷	Dominant 7th

Chord I — Tonic
Chord IV — Subdominant
Chord V — Dominant
Chord V^7 — Dominant 7th

In each family **Daughter** has a **Cousin** who can sometimes take her place when you are writing your harmonies.

Let's find **Cousin** chord. Look at the chords for all the notes of the **C Major Family**.

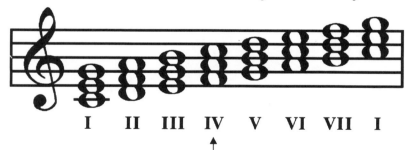

I   II   III   IV   V   VI   VII   I

Look at **Daughter** chord. Chord IV has **F** at the bottom and the notes are the same as the **Tonic** chord of **F Major**.

What is the **relative minor** of F Major? __

Look again at the **C Major Family** chords.

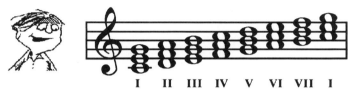

I   II   III   IV   V   VI   VII   I

Which chord in **C Major** has the same notes as the **Tonic** chord of **D Minor**? ___

 Cousin is the **Supertonic - chord II**.

When you are harmonising a melody you can sometimes use Cousin **chord II** in place of Daughter **chord IV**. Cousin can be a welcome visitor in any musical family.

Chord I	**Tonic**
Chord II	**Supertonic**
Chord IV	**Subdominant**
Chord V	**Dominant**
Chord V^7	**Dominant 7th**

Now let's learn to use **Cousin chord II.** ➡

Play these versions of a tune in **A Major**.

Did you hear in bar 2 how Cousin replaced Daughter?

Now play these versions in **B♭ Major**.

Where are the Cousin and Daughter chords?
Put **IIb** and **IV** in the correct boxes.

Meet Grandfather

In each musical family **Grandfather** may visit and take the place of **Father**.

Let's learn how to find **Grandfather** chord. Here are the chords for all the notes of the **C Major Family**. Look at **Father** chord **V**.

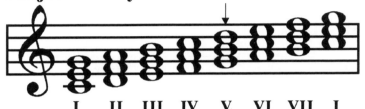

I   II   III   IV   V   VI   VII   I

Chord **V** has **G** at the bottom and the same notes as the **Tonic** chord of **G Major**.

What is the **relative minor** of G Major? __

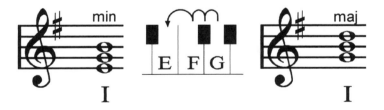

Look again at the chords in the **C Major Family**. Which chord has the same notes as the **Tonic** chord of **E Minor**? ___

Grandfather is the **Mediant** - chord **III**.

In each musical family you can have another very useful visitor. Grandfather **chord III** can sometimes replace Father **chord V** when harmonising a melody.

Chord I	**Tonic**
Chord II	**Supertonic**
Chord III	**Mediant**
Chord IV	**Subdominant**
Chord V	**Dominant**
Chord V^7	**Dominant 7th**

What about me? Isn't there someone who can give me a rest?

Soon, very soon, but let's first learn to use Grandfather's chord.

Play these versions of a tune in **A Major**.

  Did you hear in bar 1 how
Grandfather replaced Father?

Now play these versions in **B♭ Major**.

Where are the Father and Grandfather chords?
Put **V** and **III** in the correct boxes.

Grandmother Arrives

There is help at last for Mother. Her replacement is **Grandmother**.

You can discover **Grandmother** chord in exactly the same way as you discovered Cousin and Grandfather chords. Look at **Mother** chord in the **C Major Family**.

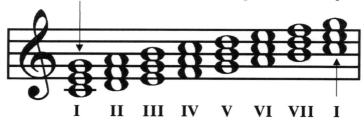

I II III IV V VI VII I

Chord **I** is the **Tonic** with **C** at the bottom.

What is the **relative minor** of C Major? __

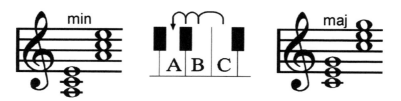

Which chord in **C Major** has the same notes as the **Tonic** chord of **A Minor**? ___

Grandmother is the **Submediant** - chord **VI**

Play these two versions of the same tune to hear how Grandmother can replace Mother.

The Grand Performance

Now play the complete piece in **A Major** using chords from the **Inner Family** only.

This version in **B♭ Major** uses the chords of our three visitors. Play it and then write **IIb**, **III** and **VI** in the correct boxes.

A Final Look Back

Match each chord with its family member.

Ic

II

III

IVc

Vb

V⁷b

VI

page 44

Family Visitors

In each musical family _____ chord IV has a cousin who can sometimes take her place. Cousin is chord ____ or the supertonic. Father chord ____ can be replaced by _____ chord ____, also known as the _____. Mother chord ____ can be substituted by _____ chord ____, also known as the _____.

10

Family Relations

Each Major Family has a Relative Minor Family with the same key signature.
You can discover the Relative Minor Family by counting down on the keyboard ____ semitones from the root note of Mother's _____ chord in the major key. For example, the relative of **C Major** is ____ **Minor**. ____ **Minor** is related to **F Major** and **A Major** to ____ **Minor**.

5

Resolving

In Book 1 you learnt that the **7th** note of
the dominant Father chord likes to fall onto
the note below. This gives a magical effect
when **chord V^7** or **V^7b** resolves **to chord I**
in a **perfect cadence**. Play and listen
carefully to these two perfect cadences.

$V \rightarrow I$ $V^7 \rightarrow I$

You also learnt in Book 1 that chords may
be **closed** or **open**. Play these two perfect
cadences in **A Major** and listen to the
difference. Circle the 7th note in each chord.

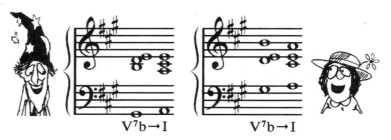

$V^7b \rightarrow I$ $V^7b \rightarrow I$

Remember the rule - we should **never
double the 7th** in a **dominant chord**.

A perfect cadence is like a 'full stop' and an **imperfect cadence** is like a 'comma' in music. Play these two imperfect cadences.

I →V   IV →V

Play the following cadences. Put the chord number in each box and write imperfect or perfect for the name of each cadence.

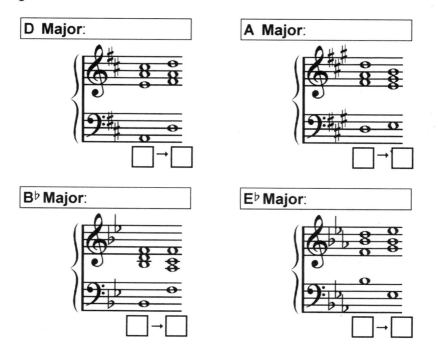

Block Chords

Play this piece in **G Major**. Notice that we have not harmonised all the melody notes.

Broken Chords and Pedalling

This version with block and broken chords ends in a **perfect cadence**.

Helpful Hints

Do **not** use chords **II**, **III** or **VI** to end a piece. Play safe by going home to Mother. Use a perfect cadence and end on the tonic.

Double the **root** or **fifth** of a chord.

Never double the **third** **except** in chord **IIb**. Chord II is often used in its first inversion.

Never double the **seventh** of a **dominant chord**.

Do **not** use chords **II**, **III** and **VI too often**. Although these minor chords add variety, they could make harmonies in major keys sound sad. You will learn about harmonies in minor keys in Book 3.

Over to You

On the following pages there are three melodies for you to harmonise.

Remember to use...

When you are satisfied with your harmonies, write them in the book.

Harmonise my tune. Draw 2/3 notes in the treble and 1 note in the bass to celebrate my special day.

IVc   I_____   V_____

IV   V   Vb   I_____   I_____

Vc   II   IIIb IVb V⁷b   I

page 52

Happy Birthday to you

Happy Birthday to you
Happy Birthday dear Grandpa
Happy Birthday to you

Kum Bah Yah

Michael, Row the Boat Ashore

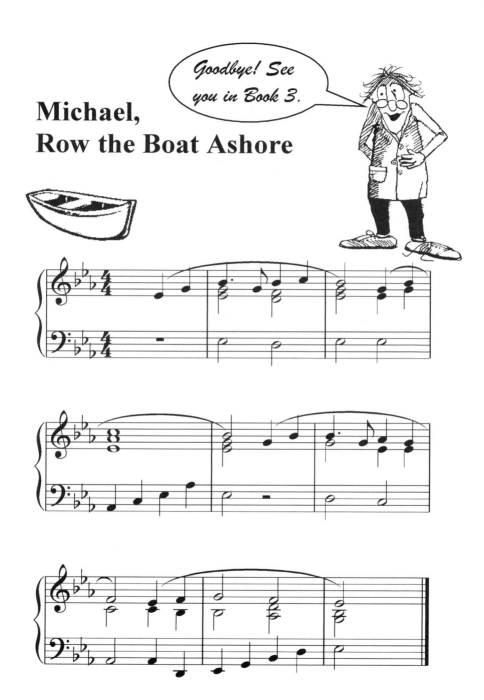

Major & Harmonic Minor Keys

Here for reference are the scales of all the keys you have met in this book. Remember in the harmonic minor scale we must raise the 7th note ascending **and** descending.

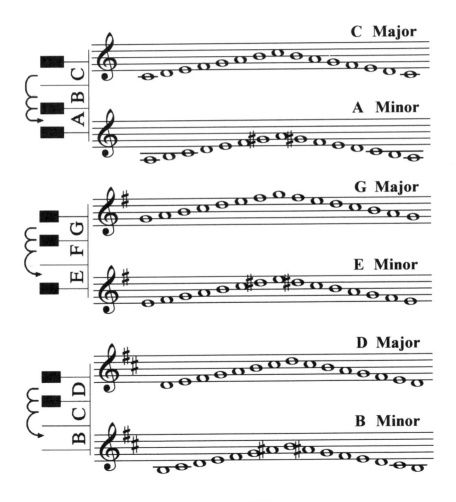

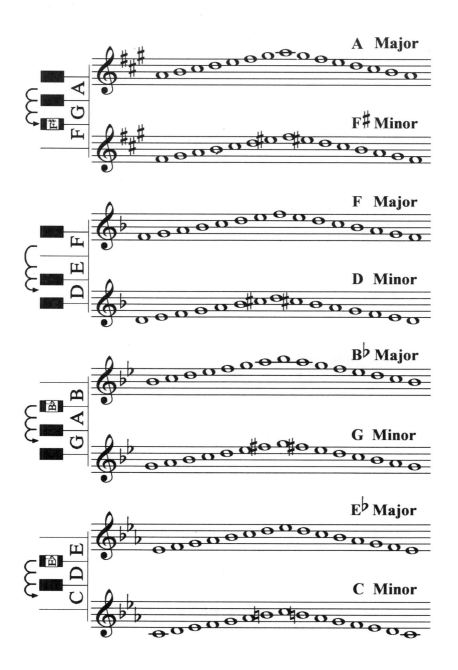

The Magic Circle of Keys

The **Major** Families on the **outside** of the circle have the same key signatures as their **Minor** relatives on the **inside** of the circle. Harmonies for **Minor** keys are in Book 3.

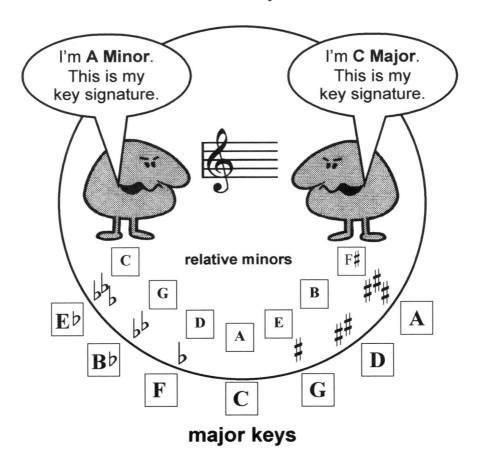

List of terms

broken chord   the notes of a chord played one after the other

cadence   the half or full close of a musical phrase or section

    imperfect   any chord going to chord V suggesting a pause for breath

    perfect   chord V going to chord I with a strong feeling of ending

    plagal   chord IV going to chord I with a weaker feeling of ending

chord   two or more notes that are played together

    in close position   the notes of a chord are as close together as possible

    in open position   the notes of a chord are spread widely

chord I (or Ia)   tonic chord in root position

    Ib   tonic chord in first inversion

    Ic   tonic chord in second inversion

    a   letter to show root position

    b   letter to show first inversion

    c   letter to show second inversion

II	supertonic chord
III	mediant chord
IV	subdominant chord
V	dominant chord
V⁷	dominant 7th chord
VI	submediant chord

II $\quad$ supertonic chord
III $\quad$ mediant chord
IV $\quad$ subdominant chord
V $\quad$ dominant chord
V^7 $\quad$ dominant 7th chord
VI $\quad$ submediant chord

Vb $\quad$ V⁷b

dominant **[Father]**	5th note of a scale and the chord grown from that note: e.g. G and G-B-D in the scale of C Major
dominant 7th	dominant chord with an added 7th note: e.g. G-B-D-F in the C Major scale
doubling	the same note (root or 5th but not usually the 3rd) used twice in the same chord
first inversion	chord with its 3rd note at the bottom
mediant **[Grandfather]**	3rd note of a scale and the chord grown from that note: e.g. F♯ and F♯-A-C♯ in the scale of D Major

resolving	movement of a note or chord to a more satisfying note or chord: e.g. chord V^7 to chord I
root	note from which a chord grows: e.g. C is the root of the tonic chord of C Major
second inversion	chord with its 5th note at the bottom
subdominant [Daughter]	4th note of a scale and the chord grown from that note: e.g. B♭ and B♭-D-F in the F Major scale
submediant [Grandmother]	6th note of a scale and the chord grown from that note: e.g. F♯ and F♯-A-C♯ in the A Major scale
supertonic [Cousin]	2nd note of a scale and the chord grown from that note: e.g. C and C-E♭-G in the B♭ Major scale
triad	a three-note chord: e.g. the tonic triad G-B-D of the G Major scale
tonic [Mother]	1st note of a scale and the chord grown from that note: e.g. E♭ and E♭-G-B♭ in the E♭ Major scale

THEORY IS FUN GRADE 1

Treble clef, bass clef, notes and letter names. Time names and values; dotted notes, tied notes and rests.
Accidentals. Tones and semitones.
Key signatures and scales (C, G, D & F Major).
Degrees of the scale, intervals and tonic triads.
Simple time signatures and bar-lines.
Writing music and answering rhythms.
Musical terms dictionary and list of signs.

ISBN 0-9516940-8-1

THEORY IS FUN GRADE 2

Major key signatures and scales to 3 sharps or 3 flats.
A, D and E minor key signatures and scales.
Degrees of the scale and intervals. Tonic triads and accidentals.
Piano keyboard, tones and semitones.
Simple time signatures. Grouping notes and rests. Triplets.
Two ledger lines below and above the staves.
Writing four-bar rhythms .
More musical terms and signs.

ISBN 1-898771-02-2

THEORY IS FUN GRADE 3

Major and minor key signatures to 4 sharps or 4 flats.
Harmonic and melodic minor scales.
Degrees of the scale, intervals and tonic triads.
Simple and compound time signatures. Grouping notes and rests. Transposition at the octave.
More than two ledger lines.
Writing four-bar rhythms. Anacrusis. Phrases.
More musical terms and signs.

ISBN 1-898771-00-6

THEORY IS FUN GRADE 4

All key signatures to 5 sharps or 5 flats. Alto clef, chromatic scale, double sharps and flats. Technical names of notes in the diatonic scale. Simple and compound time: duple, triple, quadruple. Primary triads: tonic, subdominant and dominant.
All diatonic intervals up to an octave. Recognising ornaments.
Four-bar rhythms and rhythms to words.
Families of orchestral instruments and their clefs.
More musical terms, including French.

ISBN 1-898771-01-4

THEORY IS FUN GRADE 5

All key signatures to 7 sharps or 7 flats. Tenor clef and scales.
Compound intervals: major, minor, perfect, diminished and augmented. Irregular time signatures: quintuple and septuple.
Tonic, supertonic, subdominant and dominant chords.
Writing at concert pitch. Short and open score. Orchestral instruments in detail. Composing a melody for instrument or voice. Perfect, imperfect and plagal cadences.
More musical terms, including German.

ISBN 0-9516940-9-X